Super Science

Lynn Huggins-Cooper

Wizard Whimstaff lives in a faraway land, in a magical cave. He searches for apprentices so he can pass on his powerful Science spells. This time Wizard Whimstaff has chosen you!

He has a goblin helper called Pointy, who is very clever. Pointy helps Wizard Whimstaff keep his spell books tidy. He also stirs the smelly cauldron to make scientific words appear.

Pointy has two pet frogs called Mugly and Bugly. They are very lazy. They spend most of their time eating, burping and sleeping. Their friend Miss Snufflebeam also lives in the cave. She is a little dragon. She cannot breathe fire yet, so puffs small clouds of smoke instead!

Wizard Whimstaff and his friends are very happy, solving Science problems. Join them on a magical quest to win the Trophy of Science Wizardry!

Contents

Letts

Brilliant Bodies

My name is Miss Snufflebeam.
Can you name the parts of your body?
I get them confused, but I am
sure you can help me!

arm   leg   foot

Task 1 Can you label this picture of me? Fill in the puffs of smoke using the words below.

| head | elbow | knee | stomach | neck |

a neck

d head

b

c

e

Task 2 My head hurts with all this labelling! Can you label this picture of my face for me and fill in the puffs of smoke using the words below?

| nostril | eyelid | ear | chin | cheek |

a

d

b

e

c

Task 3 Well done! Now help me to match the words to the pictures. Join the label to the part with a line.

a fingers

b toes

c nose

d elbow

e knee

f thigh

g lips

h chest

i chin

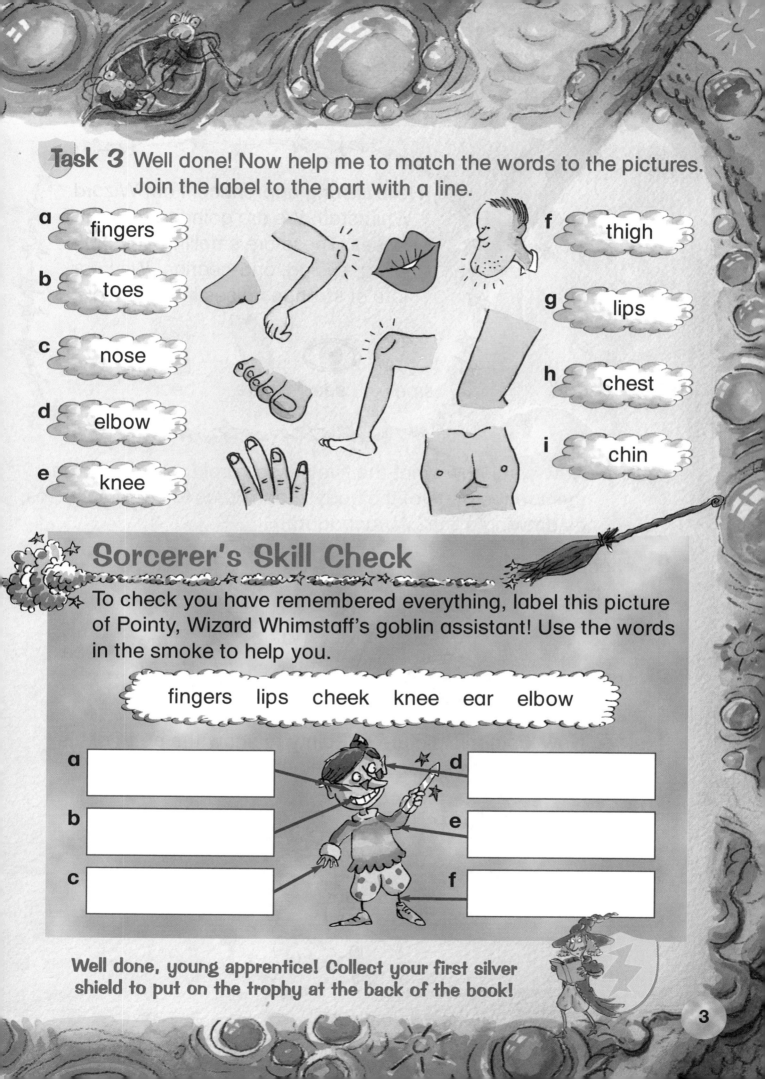

Sorcerer's Skill Check

To check you have remembered everything, label this picture of Pointy, Wizard Whimstaff's goblin assistant! Use the words in the smoke to help you.

fingers   lips   cheek   knee   ear   elbow

a

b

c

d

e

f

Well done, young apprentice! Collect your first silver shield to put on the trophy at the back of the book!

Smelly Senses

Hello, young apprentice! I am Wizard Whimstaff. We are going to look at senses. These are smelling, tasting, feeling, seeing, and hearing. We hear lots of strange noises in our cave!

smell   see   taste   hear   feel

Task 1 Now you know what the five senses are! Can you match them to the parts of the body, that help us to use our senses, by drawing a line? Abracadabra!

a hear

b taste

c smell

d feel

e see

Task 2 Now label this picture of Pointy to show the parts of his body and the senses they help him to use.

a ear — to hear

b

c

d

e

Task 3 Use your magic to draw pictures of the correct parts of the body for each sense.

a
see

b
hear

c
taste

d
smell

e
feel

Sorcerer's Skill Check

You are doing very well. For your final task, read the sentences and draw the right body part in the boxes below.

a
I help people to see.

b
You use me to smell.

c
I am used to touch and stroke.

d
I am used for listening.

e
I like to taste things!

You can add another silver shield to your trophy!
Super!

Grumpy Growing

I am Pointy, Wizard Whimstaff's assistant.
I am going to talk about growing.
When people are born, they are called babies.
They grow bigger and stronger until they
become adults, like your mum.

Pointy age 3   Pointy age 9   Pointy age 16

Task 1 Look at the pictures below. Can you put them in the right order, starting with the youngest?

a    b    c    d    e

Task 2 Well done! Now draw your own pictures to fit the labels. It is easy when you know how!

a

b

c

baby   child   adult

Task 3 Super! Now match the sentences to the pictures.

1   2   3   4   5

a I am grown-up. I can do everything for myself.

b I am nearly grown-up. In a few years I will be an adult.

c I am quite big, but still have growing to do. I can feed myself and get dressed, but need help with some things.

d I am small. I need to be fed and cannot walk by myself.

e I am not a baby, but I need lots of help with getting dressed and eating.

Sorcerer's Skill Check

Finally, answer these questions. Use the magic words on the banner to help you.

baby   teenager   toddler   adult

a I have just been born. I am a __ __ __ __.

b I am nearly grown-up. I am a __ __ __ __ __ __ __ __.

c I am grown-up. I am an __ __ __ __ __.

d I am older than a baby, but younger than a child. I am a __ __ __ __ __ __ __.

Croak! Have a shield while we have a snooze!

Charming Changes

Burp! We are the two lazy frogs called Mugly and Bugly. Frogs change from tadpoles to grown-up frogs. Baby frogs don't look anything like their parents! We are going to look at lots of babies and their parents. Here is a picture of us when we were babies.

Task 1 Croak! The babies and mums have been separated! Draw a line between the ones that match.

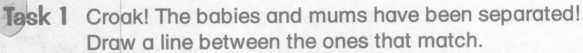

a	b	c	d	e
				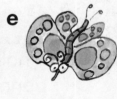

1	2	3	4	5

Task 2 Burp! We need a snack after all that work! Look at the animals in the pictures and answer the questions. Hurry, grub's up!

1	2	3	4	5

a Which babies look like their parents, only smaller?

b Which babies don't look like their parents at all?

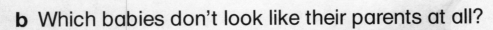
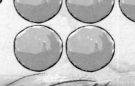

Task 3 Good work! Draw some animals in each set. You could use the pictures to help give you ideas.

babies who look like their parents

babies who don't look like their parents at all

Sorcerer's Skill Check

Slurp! Check what you have learnt so far! Draw the baby next to its mother.

a

b

c

d

e

You are clever! Give yourself another silver shield!

Amazing Alive

I am trying to work out which things are alive and which things are not alive. Living things feed, move, feel things, breathe, get rid of waste, grow and have babies. So my pet spider is alive because she does all those things!

Task 1 Sort these things into groups of alive and not alive. Draw a circle around the things that are alive.

Task 2 I am getting confused! Please answer these questions **yes** or **no** for me.

a Water moves and makes a noise. Is it alive? _____

b Wind moves and makes a noise. Is it alive? _____

c Dogs have babies, feed, move, get rid of waste, grow, feel things and breathe. Are they alive? _____

d Fire moves and makes a noise. Is it alive? _____

e Dandelions make new plants, feed, move, get rid of waste, grow and take in air. Are they alive? _____

Task 3 I wish I were as clever as you! Can you help me do some drawings for Wizard Whimstaff?

<table>
<tr><td>Draw three things that are alive in this box.</td><td>Draw three things that are not alive in this box.</td></tr>
</table>

Sorcerer's Skill Check

Can you remember which things tell us that something is alive? Use your magic to fill in the missing letters.

a f___ ___d

b m___ve

c ___eel things

d brea___ ___e

e get rid of ___aste

f gr___w

g have bab___ ___s

Excellent work, young apprentice.
Add a silver shield to your trophy!

Plant Potions

Each part of a plant has a job. The leaf makes food. The stem takes water and goodness to all parts of the plant. The flower attracts insects and the roots hold the plant in the soil. Hey presto!

Task 1 The labels are missing on this plant. Can you write new ones for me? Use the words in the box to help you.

leaf   flower   stem   roots

a

b

c

d

Task 2 Well done! Now join the labels to the job they do with a line.

a takes water and goodness to all parts of the plant

b makes food

c attracts insects

d holds the plant in the soil

leaf

flower

roots

stem

12

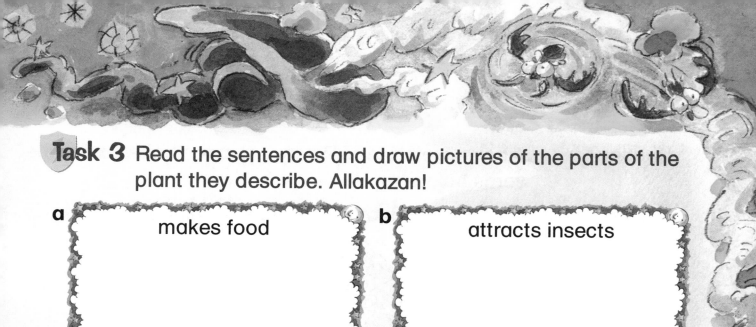

Task 3 Read the sentences and draw pictures of the parts of the plant they describe. Allakazan!

a

makes food

b

attracts insects

c

holds the plant in the soil

d

takes water and goodness to all parts of the plant

Sorcerer's Skill Check

One more thing to do! Use your magic to draw a plant and label the parts. Use the words in the box to help you.

roots

stem

leaf

flower

You are a plant wizard!
Put another silver shield on your trophy!

Apprentice Wizard Challenge 1

Challenge 1 Label this picture of Pointy. Fill in the boxes using the words below.

| head | elbow | knee | stomach | neck | fingers | toes |

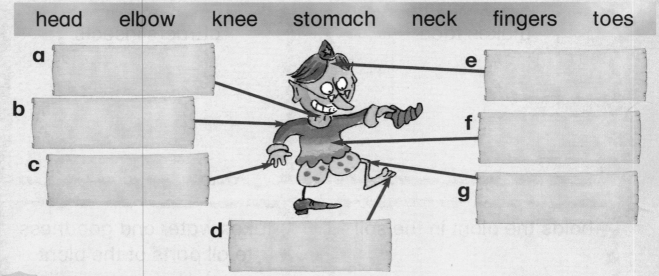

a

b

c

d

e

f

g

Challenge 2 Which body parts are we?

a I help people to see dragons and frogs. _____

b You use me to smell flowers. _____

c I am used to touch and stroke your pet bat. _____

d I am used for listening to Mugly croak! _____

e I like to taste things like beetle stew! _____

Challenge 3 Wizard Whimstaff is looking at some pictures of one his friends. Can you help him put them in order, so they show him from youngest to oldest?

a

b

c

d

e

Challenge 4 Draw the baby below its mother.

a

b

c

d

Challenge 5 Sort these things into groups of alive and not alive, by drawing a circle around the things that are alive.

Challenge 6 Wizard Whimstaff needs to collect parts of some plants for his spells. Draw a circle around the parts he wants.

a the leaf of a boggle plant

b the stem of a sherbet plant

c the roots of a wiggly bush

d the flower of a jelly plant

Put silver stars on the testometer to show how many challenges you got right. Then have another silver shield!

6

5

4

3

2

1

Challenge Score

Peculiar Plants

Croak! We like plants. They grow all around our favourite pond. Plants need sunshine and water to grow well. If plants do not get enough light, they go yellow. If they do not get enough water, they go brown and dry.

Task 1 We need lots of juicy flies and a nice damp place to stay healthy! What do plants need to grow and stay healthy? Answer these questions with true or false. Put **T** for true and **F** for false.

a Plants need water and darkness.

b Plants need to be kept dry and need plenty of light.

c Plants need to be kept dry and in the dark.

d Plants need light and water to grow well.

e Plants need wind and water to grow.

f Plants need rain and darkness.

Task 2 Answer these questions for us while we have a snooze.

a What does this yellow plant need to make it green again?

_____

b This plant is brown and dry. How can we make any new leaves green?

_____

Task 3 Burp! Draw a circle around the things a plant needs to grow.

Sorcerer's Skill Check

Check what you have learned by answering these questions.

a If a plant is yellow, what does it need to make it green again?

_____

b Why might a plant go brown?

_____

c What two things do plants need to grow?

_____ and _____

You will be as clever as Pointy soon!
Take another silver shield for your trophy!

Magical Materials

Materials means what something is made from. Stone, paper and metal are all materials. Materials have different properties. For example, they might be soft, hard, stiff, bendy, shiny or see-through.

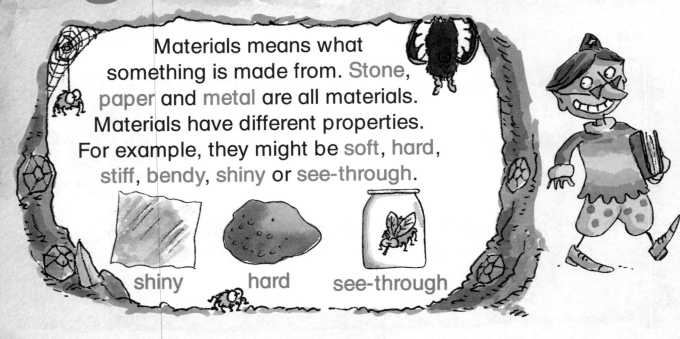

shiny   hard   see-through

Task 1 Match the object to the material it is made from. Join them with a line. Super!

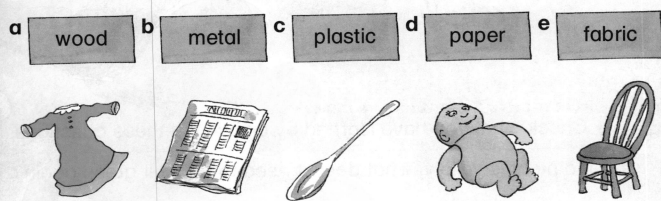

| **a** wood | **b** metal | **c** plastic | **d** paper | **e** fabric |

Task 2 This time, choose the best material to make each object. It is easy when you know how! Join them with a line.

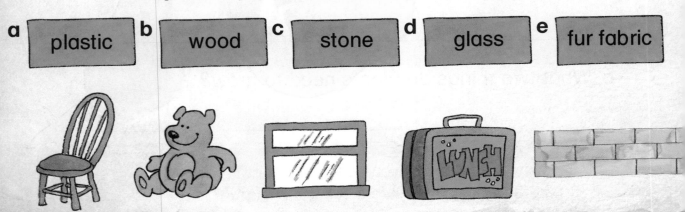

| **a** plastic | **b** wood | **c** stone | **d** glass | **e** fur fabric |

Task 3 This is a bit harder, but you will soon get the hang of it! Think about why a material is chosen to make an object. Match the reason to the object with a line.

a A car is made from metal,

because it is soft and comfortable.

b A window is made from glass,

because it is soft and cuddly.

c A dress is made from fabric,

because it is strong and tough.

d A teddy is made from fur fabric,

because it is see-through.

Sorcerer's Skill Check

A last task to check your magic skills! Write **T** for true and **F** for false.

a Stone is a material.

b The best material for a teddy is stone.

c The best material for a window is glass, because you can see through it.

d Metal is a strong material.

e Plastic is a good material for toys, because it can be made into lots of different shapes.

You are doing brilliantly! Collect another silver shield for your trophy!

Marvellous Materials

You now know lots about materials. I need your help, because I am making some things for Miss Snufflebeam's birthday. You can help me to choose the best materials for each object.

strong   soft

Task 1 First, I want to make a toy car for her to ride on. Miss Snufflebeam is quite heavy so the material must be strong. Tick the material that is best (✔).

paper ☐   wood ☐   fabric ☐   glass ☐

I also need to make the car seat comfortable. Tick the best material (✔).

paper ☐   wood ☐   fabric ☐   glass ☐

Task 2 Well done! Now, we are going to make some more things. Use your magic to choose the best materials. Write your ideas on the balloons.

a birthday card   **b** hat   **c** dress   **d** decorations

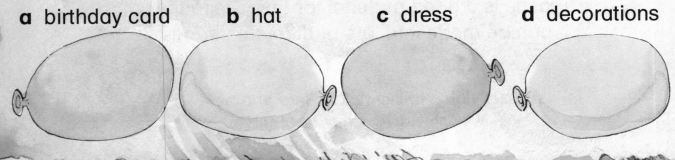

Task 3 Draw a picture of a teddy and a picture book to make for Miss Snufflebeam. Then wave your magic wand and write below the material that you would use.

teddy   picture book

material: _____   material: _____

Sorcerer's Skill Check

Let us check what you have learned. Complete the sentences by using the words on the smoke puff. Hey presto!

strong   see-through   washed

a Glass is a good material for windows, because

it is _____ _____ – _____ _____ _____ _____.

b Metal is a good material for cars, because it is

_____ _____ _____ _____ _____ _____.

c Plastic is a good material to choose for a lunchbox,

because it can be _____ _____ _____ _____ _____ easily.

Croak! Pick up another silver shield for your trophy!

Lovely Light

I have to light a lamp when the cave is dark. Objects that give off light are the sun, candles, torches, fire and light bulbs. Some things seem to give off light, but do not at all! They are just shiny which means that they reflect light, like a mirror!

Task 1 Draw a circle around the things that give off light. Hey presto!

Task 2 Well done! Now circle the thing in each pair that gives off light.

a
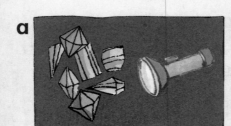

b

c

d

e

Task 3 Excellent work! Now draw a picture of all the things you can think of that make light. Look around your house to get ideas, but do not touch matches or anything else that gets hot!

Sorcerer's Skill Check

Look at the picture and draw a circle around the sources of light. Abracadabra!

Super! Put another shield on your trophy!

Playful Push and Pull

Sometimes we push and pull each other when we are playing. Today we are looking at what pushes and pulls we use every day! A push or pull can make things move or stop moving.

pull!   push!

Task 1 Croak! How do these pictures show a push?
Tell a grown-up.

a

b

c

Task 2 Now look at these pictures. How do they show a pull?
Tell a grown-up while we have a nap.

a

b

c

Task 3 Great work! Look at the list below and decide if it is push or pull. It is far too energetic for us! Circle the correct one.

a Miss Snufflebeam kicking a ball. push pull

b Pointy opening a drawer. push pull

c Mugly squeezing a sponge. push pull

d Mugly and Bugly jumping. push pull

e Wizard Whimstaff sweeping away leaves. push pull

f Miss Snufflebeam lifting the lid of a pan. push pull

Sorcerer's Skill Check

Show us what you have learned. True or false? Write **T** for true and **F** for false. Burp!

a A push can make things move.

b A push can stop things from moving.

c When you open a drawer, you pull it.

d When you close a drawer, you pull it.

e When you close a drawer, you push it.

f When you kick a ball, you pull it.

g When you kick a ball, you push it.

My head hurts with all this pushing and pulling!
Pick up another silver shield for your trophy.

25

Spooky Sounds

I hear lots of spooky sounds and I get scared! But Wizard Whimstaff says 'It's only the bats flapping', or 'That was Mugly burping!' Then I feel better!
We hear sounds when noises go into our ears. Wizard Whimstaff says sound travels through the air in waves, but I have never seen them! He says they are invisible.

Task 1 I am confused! Draw a circle around the pictures of things that make loud noises to help me.

Task 2 Now draw a circle around the things that are quiet.

Task 3 Can you read the sentences and cross out the wrong word for me?

a We hear things with our noses/ears.

b Sound travels in waves/waterfalls.

c A police car siren makes a quiet/loud noise.

d A mouse makes a loud/quiet noise when it squeaks.

e A baby makes a quiet/loud noise when it cries.

f A firework exploding makes a loud/quiet noise.

Sorcerer's Skill Check

For your last task, look at the pictures. Mark the things that make a loud noise with an **L** and the things that are quiet with a **Q**.

a   b   c   d

e   f   g   h

When we burp, we are so loud that the windows in the cave rattle! Grab another silver shield for your trophy!

Apprentice Wizard Challenge 2

Challenge 1 This plant has yellow leaves and is starting to go brown and crinkly. What has happened to it and how can we make it healthy again?

_____

_____

_____

Challenge 2 Draw a line to the best material to make each object.

a a chair for Wizard Whimstaff

b a cuddly dragon for Miss Snufflebeam

c a book about flies for Mugly

d a frog-shaped lunchbox for Bugly

e a coat for Pointy

plastic

wood

fabric

paper

fur fabric

Challenge 3 Look at this picture of a house. Use the words from the owl to label the materials that have been used.

wood   stone   fabric   glass

a wall _____

b door _____

c window _____

d curtains _____

Challenge 4 Look at the picture and draw a circle around the sources of light.

Challenge 5 Push or pull? Circle the correct one.

a Miss Snufflebeam playing tennis. push   pull

b Wizard Whimstaff opening a drawer. push   pull

c Pointy polishing the windows. push   pull

d Mugly biting a cake. push   pull

Challenge 6 Go for a 'sounds walk' with an older member of your family. When you come back, draw a picture of the things you hear.

loud sounds

quiet sounds

6

5

4

3

2

1

Challenge Score

Put silver stars on the testometer to show how many challenges you got right. Then take your final shield!

Answers

Pages 2–3
Task 1
a neck
b elbow
c knee
d head
e stomach

Task 2
a eyelid
b nostril
c chin
d ear
e cheek

Task 3
a   f
b
c   g
d   h
e i

Sorcerer's Skill Check
a cheek
b lips
c fingers
d ear
e elbow
f knee

Pages 4–5
Task 1
a   d
b   e
c

Task 2
a ear – to hear
b tongue – to taste
c fingers – to feel
d eyes – to see
e nose – to smell

Task 3
a   d
b   e
c

Sorcerer's Skill Check
a   d
b   e
c

Pages 6–7
Task 1 b d c e a

Task 2 The following are example drawings:
a

b

c

Task 3
a 1
b 5
c 3
d 2
e 4

Sorcerer's Skill Check
a baby
b teenager
c adult
d toddler

Pages 8–9
Task 1
a 4
b 1
c 5
d 3
e 2

Task 2
a 1, 3 and 4
b 2 and 5

Task 3 Many answers are possible. The following are example drawings:
'look like their parents'

'don't look like their parents'

Sorcerer's Skill Check

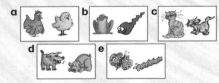

Pages 10–11
Task 1

Task 2
a no
b no
c yes
d no
e yes

Task 3
Many answers are possible. The following are example drawings:
'alive'

'not alive'

Sorcerer's Skill Check
a feed
b move
c feel things
d breathe
e get rid of waste
f grow
g have babies

Pages 12–13
Task 1

Task 2
a stem
b leaf
c flower
d roots

Task 3
a b
c d

Sorcerer's Skill Check
The following is an example drawing:

flower — leaf
stem — roots

Pages 14–15
Challenge 1
a neck
b elbow
c fingers
d toes
e head
f stomach
g knee

Challenge 2
a eyes
b nose
c fingers
d ears
e tongue

Challenge 3
b d c e a

30

Challenge 4

a  b c d

Challenge 5

Challenge 6

a 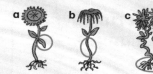 b c d

Pages 16–17
Task 1 a F
      b F
      c F
      d T
      e F
      f F

Task 2 a light
      b add water

Task 3

Sorcerer's Skill Check
      a light
      b not enough water
      c light and water

Pages 18–19
Task 1

a wood b metal c plastic d paper e fabric

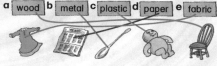

Task 2

a plastic b wood c stone d glass e fur fabric

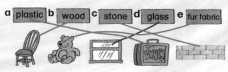

Task 3 a because it is strong and tough.
      b because it is see-through.
      c because it is soft and comfortable.
      d because it is soft and cuddly.

Sorcerer's Skill Check
      a T
      b F
      c T
      d T
      e T

Pages 20–21
Task 1 strong:

wood ✓

comfortable:

fabric ✓

Task 2 a paper or card
      b fabric
      c fabric
      d paper or card

Task 3

fur fabric   paper

Sorcerer's Skill Check
      a see-through
      b strong
      c washed

Pages 22–23
Task 1

Task 2

a  b c

d e

Task 3 Many answers are possible. The following are example drawings:

Sorcerer's Skill Check

Pages 24–25
Task 1 a The boy is pushing his car and making it move.
      b The hand is squeezing the sponge by pushing the fingers together.
      c Pointy is pushing the door and making it open.

Task 2 a Miss Snufflebeam is pulling the string and making her toy move along.
      b Pointy is pulling the drawer handle towards him to make the drawer open.
      c The hand is pulling the light cord to turn the light on.

Task 3 a push
      b pull
      c push
      d push
      e push
      f pull

Sorcerer's Skill Check
      a T
      b T
      c T
      d F
      e T
      f F
      g T

Pages 26–27
Task 1

Task 2

Task 3 The following words should be crossed out:
      a noses
      b waterfalls
      c quiet
      d loud
      e quiet
      f quiet

Sorcerer's Skill Check
      a L
      b Q
      c Q
      d Q
      e L
      f L
      g Q
      h L

Pages 27–28
Challenge 1
      It has not had enough light or water. Put it next to a window and water it.

Challenge 2
      a wood
      b fur fabric
      c paper
      d plastic
      e fabric

Challenge 3
      a stone
      b wood
      c glass
      d fabric

Challenge 4

Challenge 5
      a push
      b pull
      c push
      d push

Challenge 6
      Many answers are possible. The following are example drawings:
      'loud sounds'

      'quiet sounds'

The end

Wizard's Trophy of Excellence

Brilliant Bodies

Smelly Senses

Grumpy Growing

Charming Changes

Amazing Alive

Plant Potions

Peculiar Plants

Magical Materials

Marvellous Materials

Lovely Light

Playful Push and Pull

Spooky Sounds

Apprentice Wizard Challenge 1

Apprentice Wizard Challenge 2

This is to state that Wizard Whimstaff awards

Apprentice _____

the Trophy of Science Wizardry. Congratulations!

Published 2003
10 9 8 7 6 5 4

Letts Educational, The Chiswick Centre,
414 Chiswick High Road, London W4 5TF
Tel 020 8996 3333 Fax 020 8742 8390
Email mail@lettsed.co.uk
www.letts-education.com

Text, design and illustrations © Letts Educational Ltd 2003

Author: Lynn Huggins-Cooper
Book Concept and Development:
Helen Jacobs, Publishing Director; Sophie London, Project Editor
Design: Linda Males
Editor: Andrew Schofield
Illustrations: Mike Phillips (Beehive illustration)
Cover Illustration: Neil Chapman (Beehive illustration)

British Library Cataloguing in Publication Data

A CIP record for this book is available from the British Library.

ISBN 978-1-84315-129-6

Printed in Italy

Colour reproduction by PDQ Repro Limited, Bungay, Suffolk.